THE ADVENTURES OF SNICKLEFRITZ

BY MARGARET BECK

RoseDog Books

PITTSBURGH, PENNSYLVANIA 15238

RoseDog Books
585 Alpha Drive
Pittsburgh, PA 15238
Visit our website at *www.rosedogbookstore.com*

ISBN: 978-1-6366-1570-7
eISBN: 978-1-6366-1599-8

To Eric and Marilyn Robinson, my son-in-law and daughter, whose material and pictures have been used in this book

THE

ADVENTURES

OF

SNICKLEFRITZ

Have you ever seen a sheep dog corral the sheep in a pasture? I watched the dog one morning in the pasture where we lived and decided I could do that, too. I ran from one side of the sheep to the other, back and forth, back and forth, and when I had them all together, I sat in front of them like a general reviewing his troops. My name is Snicklefritz. I am a Canadian cat, and Canada is a beautiful county. I am a Maine Coon cat who was born on a farm near Prince Albert in Saskatchewan. My mister is a doctor who loves cats, and I'm so happy we found each other. He loves adventure like I do.

You know that cats are hunters, right? I like to catch mice and rats, and moles, and birds, and ducks and other critters. Most of them, I just let go. It is the chase that is fun. I even tried to catch seagulls once, but they are a little too big for me. I was never successful. I would jump on them, but they would just shake me off and walk away. Humph!

One time while living at the farm, I found a rat in a trap in our neighbor's barn. I didn't think it would be missed, so I brought it to my mister through my cat door. He really didn't appreciate it like I thought he would. Another time the neighbor's cat, who was my friend, was hungry. Since there were steaks cooking on the neighbor's grill, I got one of the steaks for my friend's supper. Of course he shared it with me, and it was so good.

Eventually my mister and mistress bought a forty-one-foot sailboat. They cleaned it up and decorated it and then we sailed up the strait to Campbell River, our town, and lived on the boat. One time I had a really close call. I like to wander and to hunt. There are lots of eagles in British Columbia and they are usually looking for salmon or other fish. One day an eagle swooped down as I was exploring and caught me with his claws. I was really scared. I think I was a little too heavy for the eagle to carry me very far, and he finally dropped me in the water. It is a good thing his talons didn't hurt me very much and I swam to shore as quick as I could. I decided to go home and stay out of that eagle's sight. I just gave up hunting for the day.

From Campbell River, we sailed down the Strait of Georgia to the big city of Vancouver and lived in a marina. I loved the freedom around the marina. I like to wander, and I found a ditch over across from the marina's parking lot where there were a lot of critters. I brought home two dead mice for my mister and then one dead rat for my mistress. I like to bring live critters home and let them free in the cockpit and play with them. One present for my mister was a live mouse, and for my mistress, I found a vole.

My mister and mistress decided to work in a hospital on the Island of Saipan in the Marianas. They planned to sail from Cabo San Lucas, Mexico to Saipan. It took a while to sail the boat down to Cabo, so they would take time off work, sail down the western coast of the United States, leave the boat in a marina, then fly back to Vancouver and work a while. Then fly back to the boat sail some more down the coast, leave the boat, and fly back to Vancouver to work. All this time, they would leave me with a daughter, and I was not happy! I knew my family was leaving me behind and I did not like it, so I turned into a wildcat in the car when the daughter picked me up from the marina to take me home with her.

When we reached the apartment, I found a safe place under the coffee table and threatened anyone who came close. I was so disagreeable that they finally grabbed me and shut me up in a back room. Ah, but they didn't know that I could open windows. I opened the window and convinced Macio, the daughter's housecat, to come with me. I knew the area because I had been here before. Macio and I wandered around the streets a little all night,but she got tired and decided to go home. I wandered around all day and into the night, but it started pouring rain,so I went home and walked on the daughter's head as she was sleeping to let her know I was home and that I would like something to eat, please.

After a month, my mister and mistress finally came back, and it was my time to fly with them. I was so happy to be back with my family. We were going to our boat which was now moored in California and sail the rest of the way to Cabo San Lucas. We would stay in Mexico until the hurricane season was over, then we would set sail for the Island of Saipan. This was my first plane trip. I was nestled in a nice little carrier and went as cabin luggage. Once I got used to the noises of the plane, I think I slept most of the way. When we got to Los Angeles, my mister rented a car to take us to the boat. I was happy to hop into the car when he opened my carrier, and I was especially glad to get back to my boat and my home, the *SV Finisterra.*

We left California. This was my first time sailing on the ocean and I must admit, I was a little seasick at first. Instead of a gentle rocking, we were really moving back and forth. But I finally got used to it.

My mister and mistress had prepared the boat with netting all the way around, so that I could not fall off or be thrown into the heavy seas. They thought about my safety. I could go anywhere on the boat that I wanted to, but one of my favorite places to rest was at the top of the ladder in the galley so I could watch my mistress cook. My family loves me, and I love them.

In Cabo we were moored out in the bay, and when we needed supplies, we took the dingy to shore. It was a little scary, and it took me a little while to get used to the dingy. Eventually I would walk on the beach with my mister. I knew the dingy was the way to get back to my boat. Sometimes when we were not far from the shore, I would jump into the water and swim to shore. I didn't like to get my tail wet though, so I kept it straight up like a flagpole. A heavy, wet tail makes it harder to swim.

Finally the hurricane season was over, and it was time for some serious sailing. We took on all the supplies we needed and set sail for Saipan. We were on the ocean for almost two months. Let me tell you, that was quite an experience. For the lumpy weather, my mistress fastened me into a bunk with netting, so I wouldn't get thrown around the boat. At times we had large seas and the wind gusted to thirty knots and one time it was sixty knots. That makes for some pretty big waves, and it was scary. One time we had an intense electrical storm and the whole sky was lit up by lightening. My mister shut down the computer and the radio, and I hid in my hammock. These bad times didn't last long though.

Once in a while, a flying fish would land on the boat and I would check it out. Other times I would watch my mistress cook our meals. In all the time of sailing to Saipan, only one bird landed on the boat and I had no trouble catching him. But there was usually one bird that sat at the top of the mast. I spent a lot of time calculating how I could climb up that pole and get that bird. I never did.

We had a real problem when we reached the International date line – that's when you cross an imaginary line at longitude 180 – and one side is yesterday, and the other side is tomorrow. Our automatic wind vane steering was bent by the heavy seas, and my mister and mistress were having to steer the boat by hand. They would take turns, but it was soon becoming quite exhausting. They needed some quiet water to fix the problem, and Wake Island seemed to be a good place to head for. The mother of my mistress helped us get in touch with the military on Wake Island and get approval to enter this restricted area. We arrived on Wake Island, and they had engineers and a shop where they could make a new piece for the boat. I stayed on the boat by myself the first night but then I decided I would rather be with my family. I went with them to the house where they were staying. Everything was so strange. I was really stressed and had to be right with my family. I cried and yowled when they were out of my sight. I was so glad when the boat was fixed, and we were back in our home again.

Finally we arrived on the Island of Saipan, but this is not good. I found that I had to be locked up in jail for sixty days. They had to make sure that I wasn't bringing a disease to this island that other animals could get. I could see my family for only one hour each day, from 9:00 to 10:00 in the morning. The jailers did take good care of me though, but it was boring…boring…. I heard that this island has a lot of wild cats, chickens, lizards, brown snakes, rats, and mice. Won't I have fun when I get out of this jail.

At last the day came! I had my last visit with the animal doctor and have been released to go to my new home with my family. Oh, boy! They take me for daily walks, and sometimes we are in the jungle. I have seen the wild cats, but they don't bother me, nor do the chickens or roosters or the two bulls that are near our house. The little goat finds me very interesting. He's sweet, but I don't bother him. My most fun is catching lizards. They are a good lunch. The only problem is if you hold their tail for very long, it comes off, and I have to slap my foot on them to keep them from getting away.

After a month of chasing lizards, I have found something better – rodents. They are bigger, and I like catching them and taking a present to my mister. Whoops, I notice my mistress has started closing my cat door, so I can't bring them in the house anymore. I decided I should leave their gifts at the front door.

Well, two years have passed, and I've had a terrible accident. I was attacked by three wild dogs, and three against one wasn't fair. I lost. I was terribly beaten up, and my mistress found me under a bush. They rushed me to the cat hospital, and for a week they did not think I would live. My mister and mistress were by my side giving me antibiotics and fluids and feeding me with a syringe. I needed surgery, but they had to wait until I was in better shape. Finally there was no more waiting and they must go ahead because my platelets and hemoglobin had dropped considerably and I would go to kitty heaven if they did not go ahead and do the surgery. Surgery was successful, and my family watched me very closely and took care of me. I am now on a special diet because of renal failure. I guess I am getting old. This mauling probably used up three or four or maybe more of my nine lives. I must be more careful.

Almost a year after my surgery, my family went back to Canada for the Polar Bear Swim, and their friends were house sitting and keeping me company. I couldn't go with them because when I came back, I would have to be in jail again. So jail in Canada and jail on Saipan, NO! I liked my family's friends very much and treat them the same as my family. I butt them with my head in the morning to wake them up, so they will feed me.

One day while my friends were house sitting, I snuck out of the house and climbed down the columns of the balcony and tried to chase away two dogs who were stealing the food of my two little cat friends from next door. I was a valiant defender, but the dogs were too much for me, so now my kitty spirit will tell you the rest of the story. My friends buried me in a pretty little grave next to the catamaran hull because they said I was a "salty, sailing cat." When my family left Saipan and sailed to Borneo, they dug up my casket, and at a proper time for my burial at sea, they covered my casket with the Canadian flag and as I slipped under the waves, they sang Canada's national anthem, O' Canada.

O' Canada
Our home and native land!
True patriot love in all us command.
With glowing hearts, we see thee rise,
The True North strong and free!
From far and wide,
O Canada we stand on guard for thee.
God keep our land glorious and free!
O Canada, we stand on guard for thee.
O Canada, we stand on guard for thee.

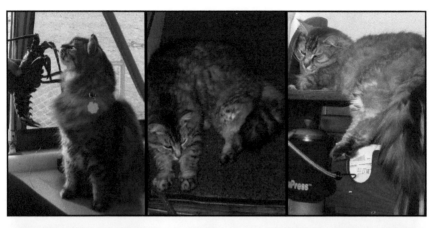

ACKNOWLEDGEMENTS

This book was promised many years ago when my daughter, Marilyn, gave me a CD with the pictures and a list of the things that Snicklefritz did. Many things got in the way of writing and the list and CD ended up in a file drawer. While being confined by Covid-19 and cleaning out the files, the folder was found, and I knew that I must make this book happen.

Thanks to my publisher and Adam and Matt for the encouragement and advice that was given to me.

CPSIA information can be obtained
at www.ICGtesting.com
Printed in the USA
BVHW020714250222
629845BV00001B/2